GUIDE FOR ROCKY SHORE INVES'.

Some guidelines to help you choose
rocky shore investigation

by
John Archer-Thomson
Dale Fort Field Centre, Field Studies Council

CONTENTS

Section 1 Introduction

This guide is designed to help you to plan and carry out a rocky shore investigation. It does not aim to tell you which investigation to choose, that is your decision. Hopefully, it will give you some ideas and some advice as to how to put these ideas into practice.

Don't be put off by the size of the guide, you don't have to read it all. Go to the section(s) you need and feel quite at liberty to ignore the rest. Sections are cross referenced; you may find it useful to read different sections at different stages of the investigation.

Now in the privacy of your own cranium

ARE YOU?........

(go to page 3)

Fanatically interested in Marine Ecology, philosophically minded and do you have plenty of time to spare?

NO

YES ⇨

Are you lying?

Read SECTION 2 and achieve complete NIRVANA

Moderately interested in Marine Ecology, practically minded, with a moderate amount of time to kill?

Be VERY **COOL**

NO

YES ⇨

Are you really this cool?

Go to the winebar, pub or SECTION 3

Quite interested in Marine Ecology, more at home with a personal stereo and in a mild panic?

NO

YES ⇨

Do you stand out in a crowd?

See Analyst quick, or go to SECTION 3

Totally uninterested in Marine Ecology, already listening to your personal stereo and looking forward to going home?

HEY MAN, LIFE'S A DRAG ISN'T IT?

NO

YES ⇨

Are you doing the right A' level?

Take a disinterested look at SECTION 3.2.4, before catching the train

Section 2 Why rocky shores?

Choosing a place to study ecology can be rather a problem. There are many suitable habitats: woodlands, grasslands, freshwater systems, the open ocean, cowpats and even the gaps between your friend's toes spring to mind. Rocky shores offer a combination of advantages that make them particularly appropriate.

The headings that have been chosen are convenient but fairly arbitrary. Ideas will obviously overlap, so inclusion under one heading will not exclude relevance under another. This discussion is necessarily general. Any individual embarking on a rocky shore investigation hopefully will find the material useful but will have to adapt it according to his or her needs.

2.1 Why ? Naturalness

It is unusual for students to be able to study a habitat which is not a reflection of interference, intentional or unintentional, by Man. For example, it is highly probable that none, or certainly very little, of the post-glacial woodland that once covered a large proportion of Britain remains. All or most of our present-day woodland has been planted at some time. Most grassland, another widely studied habitat, is the result of sustained management. Consider some of the ways that a grassland habitat may be interfered with; it may be harvested, cut, burnt, ploughed, reseeded, fertilised with organic or inorganic fertiliser, stocked with varying densities of herbivores, subject to crop rotation, artificially drained and treated with herbicides and/or pesticides. There are many effects due to a range of other human activities including walking, ball games, picnics, county shows and rock concerts. The list is very long.

Freshwater habitats are affected similarly - often indirectly by management practices (such as those described above) on adjacent terrestrial habitats.

It is difficult to find parallels for many of these activities on a rocky shore: some harvesting does occur (crabs may be taken for bait and seaweeds are collected for cosmetic, industrial and domestic uses); there are a few introduced species; there are effects from tourists and ecology students. But the list of "un-natural" disturbances is much shorter. Most of the activities that could be mentioned would only affect a small number of shores anyway.

Although it is not possible to say, with any degree of certainty, that the shores around Britain are not an expression of subtle pollution effects, the majority of rocky shores do not illustrate the obvious features associated with gross pollution. Certainly, enough rocky shores exist, which are significantly different from overtly polluted ones, for a valuable comparison to be possible.

Ecological studies in most habitats may have to allow for a plethora of management effects. Since a rocky shore is an unmanaged habitat ecological studies may be carried out in the absence of such complications. Although management effects can be used to illustrate important principles it is unusual and important to be able to carry out investigations in their absence.

2.2 Why ? Accessibility

Not only are most rocky shores a natural habitat but, since the British Isles have a high proportion of coastline in relation to their area, there are likely to be rocky shores within striking distance of most interested parties. No specialised equipment or skills are required to get on a rocky shore and problems with land ownership are rare as most of the coastline is accessible to the public by Right of Way.

In short, rocky shores are easy to visit and there are a lot of them; most other natural habitats do not share these features.

2.3 Why ? Because they are so varied

There are very few students whose attempts at stoic indifference can withstand exposure to a large crab or a wriggling eel. The response varies from unrestrained excitement to sheer terror but it never includes indifference. Many students find rocky shores interesting but in all probability few have ever wondered why. This section may provide some of the answers.

2.3.1 Richness/diversity

Rocky shores offer a tremendous variety of species for students to look at. There are examples from almost all the animal groups in a variety of guises. There is an element of surprise - where shapes and colours are often so unfamiliar that it is difficult for newcomers to decide which are animals and which are plants.

Plant groups are less well represented, but those present have a certain weird and wonderful quality that set them well apart from the "green stuff" that covers the fields. Consequently, people feel the need to know what they are ! The fact that the plants are often slimy scores points for novelty value if nothing else.

The animal and plant groups which are poorly represented on rocky shores, tend to be well represented in terrestrial habitats, *eg.* insects and flowering plants. Thus, most people are often familiar with them already; a fair selection can most probably be seen on the banks, dunes or cliff slopes that fringe the study area.

2.3.2 Compression in space

It is well known that some changes in species composition and climate are associated with altitudinal and latitudinal variation. These changes may be observed by climbing hundreds or thousands of metres up a mountain or by travelling thousands of kilometres from the equator to the North and South Poles. To do this you need to be extremely rich and it helps if you are completely bonkers.

Within a few metres vertically on the rocky shore, there exists an environmental gradient which varies from almost exclusively marine conditions at the bottom to almost exclusively terrestrial conditions at the top. Species toward the upper limit of the shore may be out of the sea for over 90% of the year, whereas those at the bottom may be exposed to air for only 1% of the time.

As a result of this compressed environmental gradient there is noticeable variation in species composition over very small vertical distances, often less than a metre, up the shore. Different organisms occupy those parts of the environmental gradient that they are able to exploit and/or in which they can survive (in the face of competition, predation etc.).

2.3.3 Physical complexity

As we have seen, rocky shores are likely to support a complex flora and fauna, even if they consist of smooth bedrock of uniform slope from top to bottom. However, the situation is further complicated by physical complexity: changes in slope and topography and the presence of rock pools, gullies, crevices and boulders. Frequent variations are often encountered within a few metres on a rocky shore.

Variations in aspect and wave action, within a few kilometres, and changes in climate and time of low water, over larger distances, will further complicate the picture.

The advantage of this kind of complexity is that it is layered, or rather it can be understood or taught in layers. Once the idea of changes in species composition with height up the shore is mastered, then the modifying influences of other factors can be considered. The depths to which the analysis is taken can vary with the interest, experience and ability of the student.

2.4 Why ? Because they are user-friendly (sic)

Rocky shores are unusual in Britain, if not unique, in their suitability for ecological investigations. As well as being natural, accessible, rich/diverse, compressed and complex they also have two other attributes which make them extremely convenient for ecological investigations.

2.4.1 Visible distributions and patterns

Most of the patterns which exist on a rocky shore are visible on the surface of the rocks - a feature which is so fundamental that it is easily taken for granted. Consider how much more difficult it is to see the distributional patterns of birds and insects in a woodland and the patterns of invertebrate distribution in the soil. Unlike woodlands, rocky shores have no deep-lying structure below the surface. Trying to map the distribution of lacustrine (lake-dwelling) or pelagic (sea-dwelling) organisms is notoriously difficult. In many cases the sampling method (if one exists) destroys any pattern which may exist.

Because virtually all of the rocky shore organisms live on, as opposed to in, the rock, patterns of distribution and abundance are "laid out" for inspection and comparison. Some of the patterns, the biological zones for example, are obvious from hundreds of metres away and visible to untrained observers.

2.4.2 Convenience in size and mobility

The size of many of the animals and plants on a rocky shore is convenient when it comes to seeing and handling them (but don't forget there are many that can't be seen - eelworms, unicellular algae, etc.). This is a particularly useful advantage for fieldwork especially as the mobility of most of the animals is rather limited. Phytoplankton, shoals of herring, tropical rain forests, elephants and aliens present rather more of a dilemma.

It is difficult to over-emphasise the importance of these last two sections. Because the patterns are easily visible and compressed within a few metres and because the organisms are of a convenient size and limited mobility, the rocky shore ecosystem is an extremely convenient one to work with. Because the distribution patterns are visible any differences in them will be easy to observe, and cause and effect will be easier to demonstrate and understand, especially at an introductory level. Manipulative experiments will also be easier; it is not difficult to keep winkles, topshells and limpets away from the plants or dogwhelks away from their prey. It would be rather less simple to keep birds and insects out of woodlands or puffins away from sand eels.

2.5 Some disadvantages

In the sections above we have seen how the richness/diversity, complexity, etc. of rocky shores offers advantages for the embryonic ecologist. It is also true, however, that despite these features a clear understanding of what is actually going on in the habitat is still a very difficult aim to achieve. Although it may seem easy to demonstrate interesting trends, phenomena, etc., it is much more demanding to provide answers and explanations. But this is a problem encountered in most habitats.

...................scratch the surface and you will unearth a whole bundle of questions.

Section 3 Possible starting points

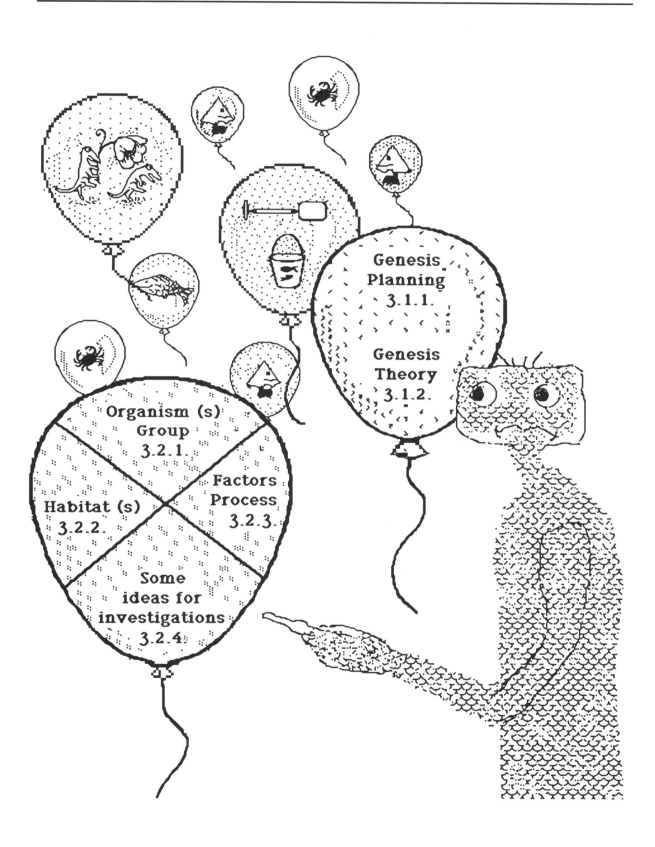

3.1 Genesis - planning and theory

3.1.1 Planning

As well as ecological or biological details you will also have to cope with practical constraints.

eg. **Time**

You may have a day, two days or a set number of periods in which to complete the work. In that time you will have to decide on an investigation, plan its execution, carry out the fieldwork, correct any disasters, write up and produce the report. Requirements will vary with your Examination Board; you should check them before you start. You may find the summary on the next page useful - tick them as you go through them.

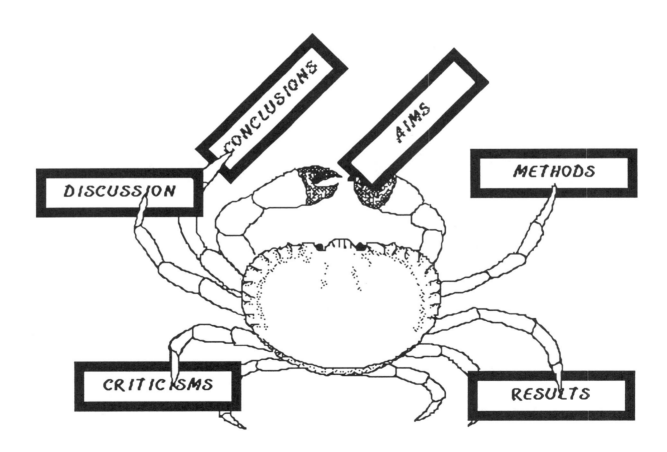

INTRODUCTION/AIMS

- ❑ Are you sure of what your aim is ?
- ❑ Have your stated your aim(s) clearly ?
- ❑ An introductory paragraph on why you decided to carry out your investigation might be useful. (See Theory/Hypothesis testing Section 3.1.2.)

METHODS

- ❑ Discuss the techniques that might be used.
- ❑ Clearly state where the work is taking place - including site, name, description, grid reference etc.
- ❑ Give your reasons for choosing the techniques.
- ❑ Are they appropriate given the aim of your investigation ?
- ❑ How many readings/samples will you need to take ?
- ❑ Does this allow a statistical treatment if appropriate ?
- ❑ If your method has limitations have you mentioned these ?

SEE - Marine Ecology notes and Section 4, *OU Project guide* (Chalmers & Parker, 1989)

NOTE - If you are going to look at 'barnacle behaviour in Force 10 storms on a wave exposed shore' you may need to refer to the safety section 5.2

RESULTS

- ❑ Are the results complete with regard to the aims ?
- ❑ Could raw data go into an appendix ?
- ❑ How will you summarise the data ?
- ❑ Consider how you could present your results in a clear, interesting, attractive (?) manner using graphs, histograms, pie charts and illustrations.
- ❑ Could you analyse your results statistically? See Section 4

DISCUSSION/CONCLUSIONS

- ❑ Discuss your results clearly and concisely.
- ❑ What can you conclude from your results with regard to your aims ?
- ❑ Don't be afraid to back up your findings with background information - (Marine Ecology notes, Library, Section 6, Tutor/Teacher)
- ❑ Have you explained any bizarre results ?

CRITICISMS/IMPROVEMENTS/FURTHER STUDIES

- ❑ If bits went "wrong" say so; how would you improve them ?
- ❑ What further studies have you suggested from your bit of work ? (Don't worry, you are unlikely to have to do them).
- ❑ If the whole lot went wrong consider a career in the Foreign Legion.

3.1.2 Theory / hypothesis testing

Many investigations, regardless of length or academic standard, have certain stages or procedures in common. You may find the format adopted below useful for structuring your thoughts.

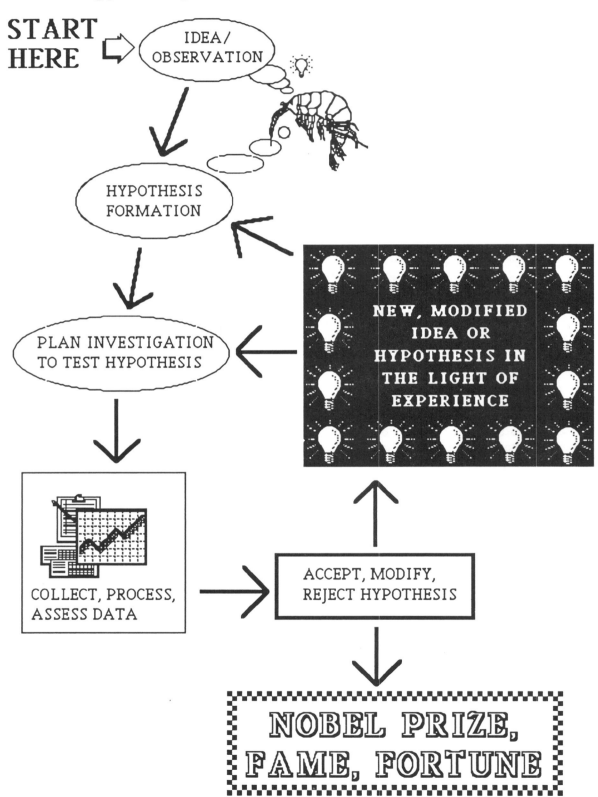

A simple example

1. Idea/observation

You fancy the local lifeguard. Further observations show that he/she is always posted on a south facing bedrock shore of moderate, uniform slope. The shore is open to both the Atlantic ocean and the prevailing wind; therefore, it is wave exposed. You also notice - during times of boredom - that the thickest clumps of seaweeds appear to be restricted to particular areas. This 'observation' leads you on to the next stage of the scientific process.

2. Hypothesis Formation (*for Seaweeds*)

You devise a hypothesis that 'explains' why seaweeds are distributed in the observed way. This hypothesis becomes the working aim of the project - you will try to show that the hypothesis can be accepted as a possible explanation, or that it is not a satisfactory explanation for the patterns seen on the seashore.

A hypothesis can be phrased in GENERAL or SPECIFIC terms

A typical GENERAL hypothesis may be :-

Exposed rocky shores are good places for seaweed

Exposed rocky shores are bad places for seaweeds.

Some examples of a SPECIFIC hypothesis:-

Seaweeds are present because:-

Sunlight and high temperature are good for photosynthesis - seaweeds grow well

Splashes keep them moist, combats desiccation.

Wind brings lots of CO_2, good for photosynthesis.

Waves knock herbivores off the rocks. Less grazing pressure on seaweeds.

Seaweeds are absent because:-

Sunlight destroys pigments. High temperature and sunlight lead to desiccation - seaweeds die.

Wave action destroys seaweeds

Wind dries seaweeds out.

Grazers present will finish off seaweeds that the wind, waves and sunlight didn't get.

A useful rule of thumb is :-

General hypotheses are easier to test - often taking less time and effort - but they are usually less interesting from a scientific point of view. If sufficient time is available it is often worthwhile to start with a general hypothesis, but combining it with a specific hypothesis which can be tested at the same time.

3. Plan investigation to test hypothesis

You decide to visit the shore at low tide to see how and where the seaweeds are distributed.

4. Collect, Process, Assess Data

You found

1   The Lifeguard was ill and had been replaced by a thin, very spotty individual who fancied you and could run faster than you!

2   There were few seaweeds.

5. Accept, Modify, Reject hypothesis

This seems to favour the second of the general hypotheses.

Having concluded that the exposed rocky shores are bad places for seaweeds you may wish to investigate which factors/processes are most significant. Your next investigation may include considerations of the relative importance of wave action, sunlight, temperature, wind effect and grazers. It may have to include little beings from Alpha Centauri who eat seaweed and can only land their solar powered craft on south facing shores. Whatever your next step is you will almost certainly go though the same stages again but from a different starting point.

This time you:

1   Are more enlightened/you have learnt something.

2   May well have noticed that the seaweeds on the exposed shore were down near the water's edge. You may wish to investigate 'why ?' *ie.* as your investigation proceeds you may actually generate more questions than you can answer.

Welcome to........

the "World of Research" !

3.2 Ecological bits

You may already have decided which organisms to study. You may find the next section useful anyway - then go to the folowing sections on habitats, processes and ideas for investigation.

3.2.1 Organisms/groups

Firstly, are you going to look at the whole rocky shore community, a few species or just one species ? If you have already decided here are a few more questions to consider.

Question/anxiety factor   **Source/answer that may offset nervous breakdown**

Can you identify it/them ? Can you classify it/them ?	☞	Keys, identification guides, Tutors, Teachers.
Do you know; will you need to know details of its/their biology and/or ecology eg.How does it feed ? 　　When does it feed ? 　　What does it eat ? 　　How does it reproduce ? 　　When does it reproduce 　　How often does it reproduce ?	☞	Marine Ecology notes, Library, Tutors, Teachers.
How does it avoid/tolerate . . . . Wave action / desiccation / thermal stress Salinity changes / pH changes	☞	Marine Ecology notes, Library, Tutors, Teachers.
What are its predators ? What are its competitors ?	☞	Marine Ecology notes, Library, Tutors, Teachers
SAMPLING STRATEGIES Does it move or not ? How many samples/readings will you take ? How will they be distributed/arranged	☞	SECTIONS 4 +6, Marine Ecology notes, Library, Tutor, Teacher
SAMPLING TECHNIQUES Does it move or not ? Is presence or absence enough ? Should you assess abundance, if so how ?	☞	SECTIONS 4 + 6, Marine Ecology notes, Library, Tutor, Teacher

THEN	**Which habitats**	☞	**SECTION 3.2.2**
	or Which factors/processes	☞	**SECTION 3.2.3**
	Some ideas for investigation	☞	**SECTION 3.2.4**

3.2.2 Habitat

"Rocky" seashores can include a variety of different 'primary' habitats, of which rocky shores and boulder shores are the two most common. Even within these two major habitats a number of more local micro-habitats exist. The table may give you some ideas for where to look and what to do.

Primary Habitat	Secondary Habitat/Microhabitat
1 Rocky Shore	*Different heights above C.D.*
	Physical zones / biological zones
	Exposed vs. sheltered -
	Grades between two extremes
	Different aspects - S. facing / N. facing comparison
	Rock Pools- same size but different height above C.D.
	- In vs Out
	Biotic / abiotic, at different heights / sizes
	Crevices
	Gulleys
	Other organisms - In, on, under associations
	Effect of Man / pollution on habitat
	Effect of freshwater run-off, streams

Primary Habitat	Secondary Habitat / Microhabitat
2 Boulder shore	*As above for rocky shores plus above and below boulder comparisons*
	Different size boulders
	Different sides of boulders / aspects

THEN having decided on Habitat :-
Which organisms/groups to study ☞ **SECTION 3.2.1**
Sample Strategy/Techniques ☞ **SECTION 4.1/4.2**
Factors/Process ☞ **SECTION 3.2.3**
Some ideas for investigations ☞ **SECTION 3.2.4**

3.2.3 *Factors/processes*

Here is a selection of ideas starting from a *Factor* or *Process*

ABIOTIC FACTORS/ PROCESSES	IDEAS FOR INVESTIGATION
Tidal Cycle/ Immersion-Emersion time	*Primary abiotic factor, affects all others, obviously varies with height on the shore.*
Water loss/desiccation	*Rate of, tolerance and/or avoidance in various organisms.*
Wave action	*Shores of different exposure, different heights on the shore(s), effects on certain species/communities, Biological Exposure Scales.*
Water movements, currents, scouring, surge gulleys siltation/turbidity	*Possible effects on distribution/ abundance of species/communities.*
Wind	*Speed, direction, duration, temperature and desiccation effects. Behaviour effects.*
Light	*Quantity - Too much, too little on species/ communities.* *Quality - Different wavelengths of light at different depths, different wave-lengths with pollution, water quality/source. Effects of waves.*
Temperature, Salinity pH,$[O_2]$,$[CO_2]$	*Changes/fluctuations - with tides, daily and seasonally. Range and optima. Avoidance/tolerance. Stress - lethal,sub-lethal effects. Rates of change. Rock pools.*
Topography	*Structural diversity of shore, habitats, micro-habitats, effects on other abiotic factors eg. wave action, drainage.*

BIOTIC FACTORS/ PROCESSES	IDEAS FOR INVESTIGATION
Competition	*Intraspecific, interspecific, scramble, resource.* *Variations in intensity with height above C.D., with exposure to wave action, with time of year.* *Mobile versus immobile.* *Effects of life cycle / reproductive method and rates.* *Competition for space, food, light, mates...etc*
Predation/ Grazing pressure	*Types of predators* **Marine** *- crabs, anemones, fish, whelks, nudibranchs, starfish.* **Terrestrial** *- birds, Man.* *Refuges from predators, disruption of search image by aggregation, prey preference, predator / prey interaction, switching to different types of prey.* *Types of grazers (winkle, topshell, limpet).* *Tolerance or avoidance by algae.* *Height on shore. Type of shore.*
Associations	*Benefits / deficits. Parasitism, mutualism, commensalism, symbiotic relationships.* *Variations with type of shore, height on shore*

Then having decided which factor/process

Organism/groups to study	☞	SECTION 3.2.1
Sample strategy techniques	☞	SECTION 4.1/4.2
Habitat	☞	SECTION 3.2.2
Some ideas for investigation	☞	SECTION 3.2.4

3.2.4 *Some ideas for investigations*

1) **Desiccation rates** in different algae (Seaweeds) under different conditions *eg.* relate the desiccation rate of brown seaweed to position on shore/species.
2) **Size of algae** - relate to position on shore - time available for photosynthesis. Compare different species, and/or one species in different positions.
3) **Age stands/ number of bladders** in *Ascophyllum nodosum*.
4) **Size/density/distribution/habitat** of individuals at different heights or on shores of different exposure/aspect/topography (limpets, topshells, anemones, mussels, etc.) Size/density of filter feeders at different heights etc.
5) **Habitat fidelity/rigidity** with different heights on the shore, aspects etc. (*eg.* sponges).
6) **Height/base ratio of limpets** - Height above C.D/exposure to wave action.
7) **Home scar returns in limpet** (over tidal cycle).
8) **Orientation of limpets** on different shores.
9) **Colour of snails** (*eg.* periwinkles) relative to height on the shore/habitat/foodstuffs etc.
10) **Age structure of topshell** (*Monodonta* spp.) populations on different shores.
11) **Dogwhelks' adhesive power** in relation to aperture size.
12) **Shell morphology in dogwhelk** on shores of different exposure.
13) **Prey/feeding preference** in dogwhelks and anemones.
14) **Nearest neighbour analysis** on anemones. Minimum distance *vs* size. Rates of tentacle retraction *vs* size of anemone.
15) **Dispersal patterns** in various populations. Variation with scale of study, height on store, detail of habitat, food supply, *eg. Spirorbis* spp. worms' density on *Fucus* spp.
16) **Associations** - Types and numbers of associations at different heights on different shores etc. Benefits/deficits to each partner.
17) **Rock pools** - Same size/different heights, abiotic/biotic interaction. Different sizes/same height, different shores.
18) **Rock pool content** *vs* adjacent rocks at different heights on the shore.
19) **Intensive study of large pool**. Zonation, profile, abiotic influences etc.
20) **Changes in community composition** with height on shore, topography, exposure to wave action, aspect.
21) **Changes in community composition** on polluted *vs.* unpolluted shore.
22) **Effects of pollution** on individuals/populations *eg.* limpets.
23) **Effects of different types of pollution** on the above.
24) **Does pollution affect the apparent BES grade** (see 27 below)?
25) **Mark and recapture studies** on various populations *eg.* crabs, sandhoppers, blue whales.
26) **Incidence of *Sacculina carcini* parasitism** in *Carcinus maenus* in relation to carapace size, sex, height on shore.
27) **Have any of the shores changed their Ballantine's exposure scale** (BES) since the original surveys were carried out (in the 1960s) ?
28) **Feeding relationships/Foodwebs** at different heights, on different shores, in different pools, in vs out of pools.

....etc. etc. etc.

Section 4 Sample Strategies and techniques

This section describes some of the strategies and techniques used in ecological sampling. The distinction between strategy and technique may not be clear - but there is an important difference. The strategy should consider how many samples to take and where and when they should be taken. The techniques are the methods by which the actual sampling is carried out. I have included a wide range of techniques and not only those relating to rocky shores. You may be able to adapt them for your investigation, even though they are not standard rocky shore techniques. This section is nowhere near comprehensive, further texts are recommended for detail.

4.1 Strategies

DO YOUR STUDY ORGANISMS MOVE ?

[1] NO
eg. plants, barnacles

(See below)

[2] YES
eg. sandhoppers, cheetahs
& traffic wardens
(Go to page 23)

[1] NO = IMMOBILE

(In the short-term this category includes most rocky shore invertebrates.)

How many Samples ?

This is extremely variable, depends on type of study and subsequent analysis
- Statistics ?

May involve pilot study
eg.. ....

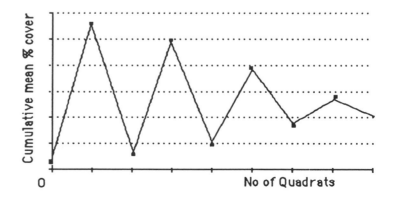

As you take more samples there appears to be less 'variability' in the results (ie. if you are averaging the total results after each batch of samples). When the fluctuation in the cumulative score has nearly disappeared, that is the ideal number of samples to take.

Remember!!

More samples = closer accuracy; therefore, probability of 'chance' result decreases.

How are the samples distributed ?

**RANDOM,
SYSTEMATIC,
STRATIFIED RANDOM,
ASSOCIATION STUDIES**

Random

Overcomes problem of hidden bias often present in Man-made habitats. Suitable when there is NO obvious environmental gradient. *eg.* some grasslands, woodlands, mudflats

Each sample point within the study area must have an equal chance of being sampled, each time. *eg. . .*

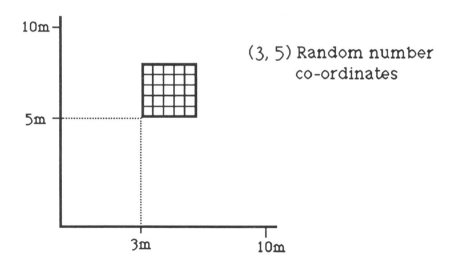

(3, 5) Random number co-ordinates

NOTE The time honoured method of throwing the quadrat over your shoulder *is not random*. It is surprising how many times the quadrat will fall in the same place - probably resulting from a combination of influences: strength, dislike of the person immediately to your left, etc. At the very least it may also kill birds and other ecologists. Use random number tables to make your random co-ordinates.

Systematic — Samples are taken at regular intervals, throughout the sample area. Used where there is an obvious environmental gradient *eg*. . . . .

THE ROCKY SHORE!

TRANSECTS - Various kinds of sample points taken along an environmental gradient

(i) *Line transects* - Record species at intervals along tape (every 5 cm.?)
Presence/Absence

(ii) *Belt transects* - Sample line has a width, may be sampled in a continuous or interrupted fashion. Intervals may be vertical or horizontal as appropriate. Easy to assess relative abundance here.

Stratified random — Select sample areas systematically and sample randomly within them. *eg*. comparison of two grassland or mudflat areas.

Association studies — Presence or absence data obtained from quadrat sampling can be used to determine whether two species are positively or negatively associated or not. *eg*. . .

		SPECIES A	
		PRESENT	ABSENT
Species B	PRESENT	No of quadrats with both present	A - Absent B - Present
	ABSENT	A - Present B - Absent	Neither Present

Results may be analysed using the chi-squared (χ^2) test
NOTE There are a large range of other association tests; see reference section for details (page 31).

[2] YES=MOBILE

Here you need to know where and when to sample as well as how; *eg.* if you are studying vampires then Transylvania and at night (though you would be much more successful at finding the real thing in South America).

eg. **VERTEBRATES** - especially birds and mammals, techniques often skilled, require expensive equipment and/or skill and licenses. If in doubt ask advice.

eg. **INVERTEBRATE TECHNIQUES** (Generally but not exclusively for Invertebrates) -

ABSOLUTE DENSITY METHODS

Direct Estimates of Total numbers
I   Nos/Microstand *eg.* number of woodlice per log
II   Nos/Unit area *eg.* aphids per leaf
III   Nos/Unit volume in liquid, soil, leaf litter

Indirect Estimates of Total numbers
I   Mark and recapture; *eg.* crabs, sandhoppers
II   Bailey Triple Catch, extension of [I]
III   Removal sampling

RELATIVE DENSITY METHODS

Direct Estimates of Relative abundance
Traps, nets, catch/unit effort

Indirect Estimates of Relative abundance
Faecal count

(See texts listed on Page 31; *eg. The OU Project Guide* for a more extensive description of all sampling strategies and methods)

4.2 Sampling techniques

DO YOUR STUDY ORGANISMS MOVE ?

[1] NO	**[2] YES**
eg. plants, barnacles	*eg*. sandhoppers, cheetahs
	& traffic wardens
(See below)	(Go to page 26)

[1] NO = IMMOBILE

Measurement of relative abundance

Density	Number per unit area or volume. Best with discrete individuals of more or less equal size.
Percentage cover	Assess area of ground shaded by selected species, usually in a quadrat. Useful if "individuals" don't exist (*eg*. sponges), or are difficult to count (*eg*. barnacles).
Percentage frequency	How many sample areas - *eg*. quadrats - contain individuals of a selected species.
Biomass **Yield** **Size**	(See *The OU Project Guide* , Ecological Methods for details, or Tutor)

Subjective methods

Species list	Useful introduction, very little more !
A.C.F.O.R	Five point scales (sometimes more, commonly used in rocky shore work as a measure of relative abundance). (See Marine Ecology notes)

Quantitative methods - quadrat techniques

Frame Quadrat   Sample area is usually a square but need not be. Note: the size of the quadrat may affect results.

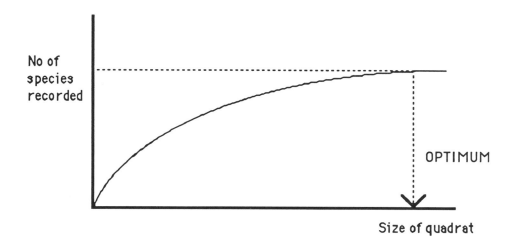

Point Quadrat   Each pin is essentially a very small quadrat measuring presence or absence of each species. A quick method, tends to miss rare species.

[2] YES=MOBILE

Invertebrates and free floating plants in aquatic habitats

Nets of various kinds	(i) Plankton, Nekton - swept or dragged through the water.
	(ii) Benthos - Drag net across bottom. Kick sample where there is a current.

Invertebrates in the air or on vegetation

Various methods	(i) Pooter
	(ii) Sweep net
	(iii) Beating tray, sheet
	(iv) Sticky trap
	(v) Water trap
	(vi) Light trap

Invertebrates in soil or leaf litter

Various methods	(i) Pitfall trap
	(ii) Chemical trap
	(iii) Tullgren funnel

(See text listed on page 31 - *eg. The OU Project Guide* - for more extensive description of all sampling strategies and methods.)

Section 5   Code of conduct & safety

5.1 Code of conduct on the shore

The Field Studies Council operates to increase environmental awareness, this involves encouraging a respect for all forms of life (except perhaps mosquitoes, horseflies and viruses). The shores of Pembrokeshire are used continually and heavily both by students from the FSC Centres and from many other bases in the country. They could become seriously damaged, we therefore ask you to observe the following code :-

5.1.1. Collecting
Avoid collecting specimens unless it is absolutely necessary. If you need to collect, keep numbers to a minimum. **Do not collect** rarer species.

Ensure that, whenever possible, collected specimens are kept alive and healthy. Return them to the same shore and to the same habitat when you have finished with them.

DO NOT COLLECT

Do not collect from the sites listed below, as they are used regularly for surveys and monitoring.
Black Rock (Dale Village)
Watwick Bay (North Side)
Castlebeach Bay
Frenchmans Steps Shore and 100m either side
Point Wood Beach
St. Bride's Haven

The Skomer Marine Nature Reserve includes the mainland areas of Martins Haven and the north end of Marloes Sands. Collecting from these sites is **strictly forbidden**.

Please **do not** collect dogwhelks from Dale Roads as number are seriously depleted.

5.1.2 Plants

Do not rip up seaweeds or lichens to identify them. Either ask a tutor or, as a last resort, bend down and have a good look at them with a hand lens. If bending down is a problem consider giving up fieldwork or changing your jeans.

5.1.3 Animals

Do not be a thug. Kicking limpets off the rocks is destructive and stupid, and people with an I.Q. of 40 or more should find this activity well below their amusement threshhold.

If you pick up snails to have a peep at them put them back where you found them. Sunbathing is not high on their list of survival strategies.

5.1.4 Habitats

If you turn stones or boulders over, replace them again. As you can imagine suddenly being strapped to the roof of your house is a rather different proposition to a cosy evening in the basement.

Do not urinate in Rock Pools. Apart from causing a small scale environmental catastrophe, there are fish and crabs with sharp teeth and claws that may make you regret your choice of urinal ....hopefully!

5.2 Safety on the shore

5.2.1 Tides
Check the tides, do not get cut off by incoming tides. Preferably work on a falling tide.

5.2.2 Weather
Rain and strong winds can make the shore a very dangerous place to work on. Be careful of slippery rocks, seaweed and lichens. Watch out for waves, some are much bigger than others. If in doubt don't work on the shore (do some background research instead). Ask for a forecast from your Tutor or the Coastguard

5.2.3 First Aid
Take a First Aid Kit with you. Know what to do in the event of an emergency. Apply First Aid if you are trained; if not, get help immediately. Get help soon anyway

Never Work Alone

Never Work Alone

Never Work Alone

5.2.4 Signing Out / In
Sign out or tell someone (Tutor) where you are going and when. Tell them when you expect to return. Be back by the latest return time and make sure you have signed in or told the Tutor of your safe return.

5.2.5 Common Sense

"The Marine environment is full of hazards for the unsuspecting". Use your common sense, if it looks dangerous don't go there. Don't attempt complicated gymnastic routines on the rocks, if you need to play go to a supervised beach.

5.2.6 Clothing

Make sure you have warm and waterproof clothing with you. Hypothermia can kill or make you more likely to slip off the rocks. In the summer, if we have one, take plenty of clothes to cover you up before you burn, also take plenty of suntan cream. Being accused of being a fairy is better than sunburn or skin cancer.

5.2.7 Footwear

Stilettoes are not the best shoes to wear. Try to have footwear with non-slippery soles and good grips. Saltwater rots leather and stitching, so think before you decide to destroy your £100 walking boots. Strong Trainers are just about the business.

5.2.8 Others

If you see others in trouble don't laugh (at least not loudly). Go and see if they need assistance. If they do call the Tutor or Coastguard.

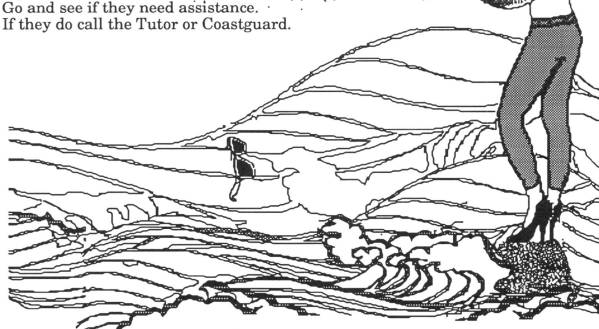

Section 6 More stuff - revelations

Some people really hate doing their projects; they go off and become Rock Stars and live in night clubs and die very rich.

Other people really do enjoy doing their projects; they live a clean, healthy and rugged life and get a good suntan. If you are one of these people here is some more stuff that you may find useful and/or interesting.

Directly related to rocky shore investigations

Bailey, N. T. J. (1981). *Statistical methods in biology*. Hodder and Stoughton, London.
Bennett, D. P. and Humphries, D. A. (1974). *Introduction to Field Biology*. Edward Arnold, London.
Chalmers, N. and Parker, P. (1989). *The Open University Project Guide: Fieldwork and statistics for ecological projects*. (2nd Edition). Occasional Publication No.9, Field Studies Council
Crothers, J. H. (1981:1987). On the graphical presentation of quantitative data. *Field Studies* **5**: 487 - 511 (available as an offprint from the Field Studies Council).
Gilbertson, D. D., Kent, M. and Pyatt, F. B. (1986). *Practical Ecology*. Hutchinson, London.
Quigley, M. and Crump, R. (1986). *Animals and plants of rocky shores*. Blackwell Habitat Field Guides. Blackwell, Oxford.
Southwood, T. R. E. (1966). *Ecological Methods*. Chapman and Hall, London.

General interest: Indirectly related to investigations

Barrett, J. (1974). *Life on the sea shore*. Collins, London.
Barrett, J. and Younge, C. (1958). *Pocket Guide to the Sea Shore*. Collins, London.
Campbell, J. (1978). *An introduction to Marine Science*. Blackie, London.
Campbell, A. C. and Nicholls, J. (1976). *Hamlyn Guide to the Sea Shore*. Hamlyn, London.
Younge, C. M. (1976). *The Sea Shore*. New Naturalist Series. Collins, London.

More academically orientated: Indirectly related to investigations

Barnes, R. S. K and Hughes, R. N. (1982). *Marine Ecology*. Blackwell, Oxford.
Brehaut, R. N. (1982). *The Ecology of Rocky Shores*. Institute of Biology Series No. 139. Edward Arnold, London.
Dring, M.J. (1982). *The Biology of marine plants*. Contemporary Biology Texts. Edward Arnold, London.
Kinne, O. (Ed.) (1970-86). *Marine Ecology* .(Vols I-V). John Wiley, London.
Lewis, J. (1964). *The Ecology of Rocky Shores*. English University Press.
Moore, P. G. and Seed, R. (1986). *The Ecology of Rocky Coasts*. Hodder and Stoughton, London.
Newell, R. C. (1978). *Biology of intertidal animals*. Marine Ecological Surveys.
Nicholls, J. (1967). *Biology of marine animals*. Pitman, London.
Tait, R. V. (1981). *Elements of Marine Ecology*. Butterworth, London.

The Field Studies Council's publications and Aidgap guides are good for ideas, background information and help with identification.